Name

Address

Blank Classic

Dotted Bullet Journal (*Light Pink*)
245 numbered pages - 252 total pages
Large 8.5 x 11

Blank Classic

Mailing address:
Blank Classic
PO BOX 4608
Main Station Terminal
349 West Georgia Street
Vancouver, BC
Canada, V6B 4A1

Cover design by: A.R. Roumanis

ISBN: 978-1-77437-166-4

FIRST EDITION / FIRST PRINTING

— Contents —

Page	Topic

— Contents —

Page	Topic

— Contents —

Page	Topic